Geometry: properties of 2D and 3D shapes

 Helpful Hint

Here are some of the shapes that you might need.

| Cuboid | Cone | Square-based pyramid | Triangular-based pyramid | Cylinder | Sphere |

 Right-angled triangle
a triangle with one right angle

 Equilateral triangle
a triangle with three equal sides

 Isosceles triangle
a triangle with two equal sides

 Rhombus
a **parallelogram** with four equal sides. Opposite angles are also equal

 Parallelogram
a four-sided shape in which opposite sides are parallel and equal. Opposite angles are also equal

 Trapezium
a four-sided shape in which two sides are parallel

 ...

 Pentagon
a shape with five sides

 Hexagon
a shape with six sides

 Heptagon
a shape with seven sides

 Rectangle
a four-sided shape with four right angles. Opposite sides are parallel and equal; **adjacent** sides are unequal

 Quadrilateral
a shape with four sides

 **Kite**
a four-sided shape with diagonals crossing at right angles

Ⓐ Answer these questions. You do not need to show your workings out.

1 What is the name of a shape with three sides, two of equal length?

_____ ☐ [1]

2 What is the name of a shape with four sides and four right angles?
The sides are not all the same length.

_____ ☐ [1]

3 What is the name of a shape with seven sides?

_____ ☐ [1]

4 What is the name of a shape with only one surface?

_____ ☐ [1]

5 How many **edges** are on a cuboid?

_____ ☐ [1]

6

What is the special name of this **prism**?

_____ ☐ [1]

Bond
No.1 for exam success

SATs Skills

Maths Workbook
Measurement,
Geometry & Statistics

10–11 years

OXFORD
UNIVERSITY PRESS

Great Clarendon Street, Oxford, OX2 6DP, United Kingdom

Oxford University Press is a department of the University of Oxford.
It furthers the University's objective of excellence in research, scholarship,
and education by publishing worldwide. Oxford is a registered trade mark
of Oxford University Press in the UK and in certain other countries

First published in 2017

British Library Cataloguing in Publication Data
Data available

978-0-19-274965-9

10 9 8 7 6 5 4 3 2

Paper used in the production of this book is a natural, recyclable product
made from wood grown in sustainable forests. The manufacturing process
conforms to the environmental regulations of the country of origin.

Printed in China

Acknowledgements

Cover illustration: Lo Cole
Page make-up and illustrations by Aptara

Although we have made every effort to trace and contact all copyright
holders before publication this has not been possible in all cases. If notified,
the publisher will rectify any errors or omissions at the earliest opportunity.

B Answer these questions. You do not need to show your workings out.

1

What is the name of this shape?

_____ [1]

2 What is the name of a rectangle with all the sides of equal length?

_____ [1]

3

What is the name of this shape?

_____ [1]

4

| Shapes with four sides of equal length | Shapes with four equal angles |

Place the following letters in the correct place on the **Venn diagram** above, according to their properties. [4]

L: square   *N*: rhombus

M: rectangle   *P*: parallelogram

5 Which three four-sided shapes have diagonals which cross at right angles?

_____ [3]

10

ⓒ Answer these questions. You do not need to show your workings out.

1 What is the name of a shape with four triangular **faces** and one square face?

_____ ☐ [1]

2 What is the name of a trapezium with two pairs of parallel sides?

_____ ☐ [1]

3 What is the name of a solid with only one edge?

_____ ☐ [1]

4 What is the name of a solid with six edges?

_____ ☐ [1]

5 Which three shapes are being described?
Has four equal straight sides with four right angles.

_____

Has four sides all of equal length, with two pairs of matching angles.

_____

Has four sides with adjacent sides being equal and only one line of symmetry.

_____ ☐ [3]

☐ 7

Geometry: 2D and 3D shapes including nets

Examples

1 Draw a triangle with sides 10 cm, 8 cm and x cm, with an angle between the 10 cm and 8 cm sides of 37°.
What is the length of the third side x?

Method:

Draw the longest side.
Measure and mark the angle at one end of the line.
Draw in the second side.
Measure the third side.

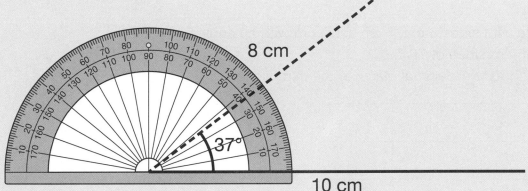

8 cm

37°

10 cm

Answer: x = 6 cm

2 Here is the net of a die.

Draw in the missing dots on the cube.

Method:
Imagine which edges would be touching when the net is folded up.

Answer:
4 dots

Ⓐ Answer these questions. You do not need to show your workings out.

1 Draw an equilateral triangle with a base of 4 cm. All interior angles are 60°.

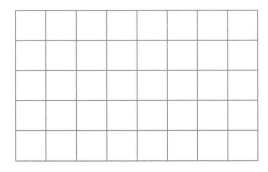

▢ 1 square = 1 cm

What is the height of the triangle to 1 decimal place?

_____ cm ▢ [1]

▱ 1

2 Draw the net of a square-based pyramid with a base edge of 2 cm. The pyramid is 2 cm tall.

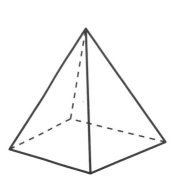

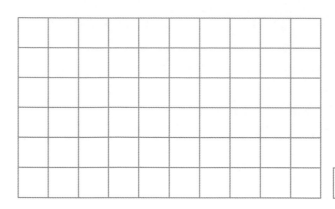

1 square = 1 cm

[1]

3 Draw a triangle with sides 6 cm, 5 cm and x cm with an angle between the 6 cm and 5 cm sides of 70°.
What is the length, to 1 decimal place, of the third side x?

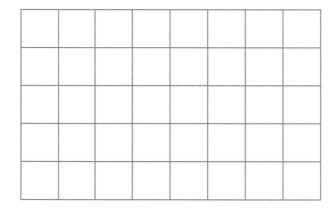

_____cm [1]

B Answer these questions.

1 Draw an isosceles triangle with sides 8cm, x cm and x cm with two angles of 30°.
What are the lengths, to 1 decimal place, of the second and third sides x?

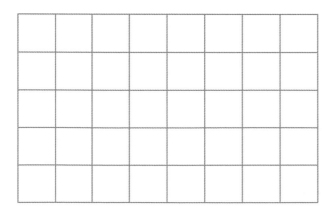

_____cm [1]

3

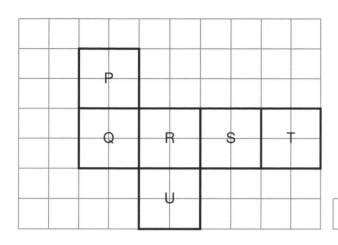

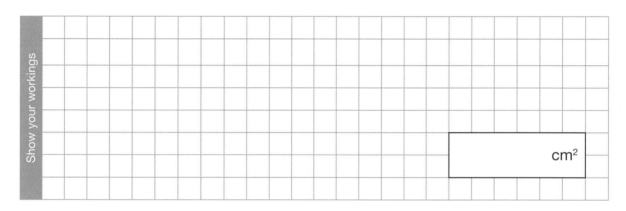

1 square = 1 cm

2 What is the **surface area** of the cube shown above?

cm² [1]

3 What is the **volume** of the cube shown above?

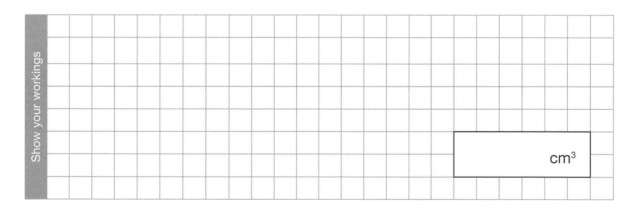

cm³ [1]

4 Which face is opposite face T when the cube is constructed? _____ [1]

5 Which face is opposite face U when the cube is constructed? _____ [1]

4

ⓒ Answer these questions. You do not need to show your workings out.

1 Draw a parallelogram with all sides of 6 cm.
Two of the interior angles are 60°.
What is the shortest distance between each pair of parallel sides, to 1 decimal place?

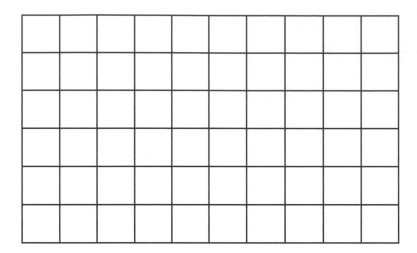

_____cm ☐ [2]

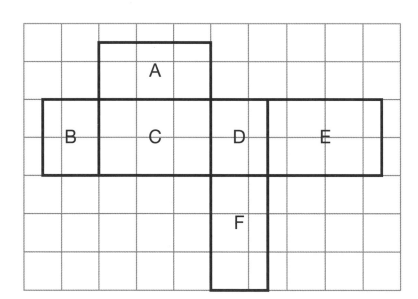

2 What is the surface area of the cuboid shown above? _____cm² ☐ [2]

3 What is the volume of the cuboid shown above? _____cm³ ☐ [2]

4 Which face is opposite face *E* when the cuboid is constructed? _____ ☐ [1]

5 Which face is opposite face *A* when the cuboid is constructed? _____ ☐ [1]

8

Geometry: angle properties

 Helpful Hint

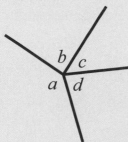

Angles at a point add to 360°
$a + b + c + d = 360°$

Vertically opposite angles are equal

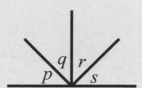

Angles on a line add to 180°
$p + q + r + s = 180°$

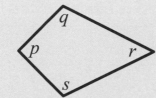

Angles in a quadrilateral add to 360°
$p + q + r + s = 360°$

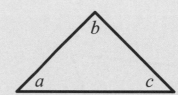

Angles in a triangle = 180°
$a + b + c = 180°$

Shape	Total interior angles
Triangle	180°
Quadrilateral	360°
Pentagon	540°
Hexagon	720°

(A) Find the missing angles. Diagrams not drawn to scale. You do not need to show your workings out.

1

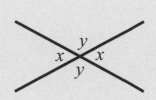

120°
40°
$x°$
100°

$x = $ _____ ° ☐ [1]

☐ 1

2

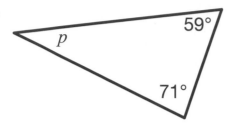

y = _____ ° ☐ [1]

3

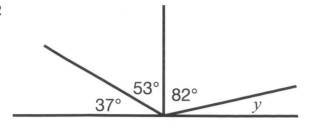

p = _____ ° ☐ [1]

4

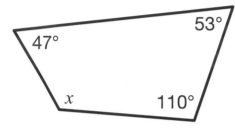

x = _____ ° ☐ [1]

5

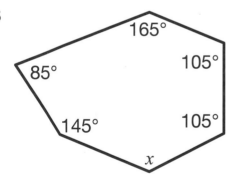

x = _____ ° ☐ [1]

(B) Find the missing angles. Diagrams not drawn to scale.
You do not need to show your workings out.

1

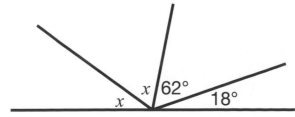

x = _____ ° ☐ [1]

☐ 5

2

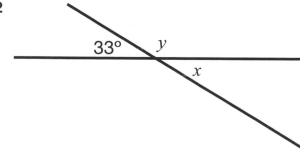

$x =$ _____ ° $y =$ _____ ° [1]

3

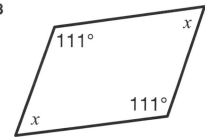

$x =$ _____ ° [1]

4 Here is a regular pentagon. Find the size of each interior angle p.

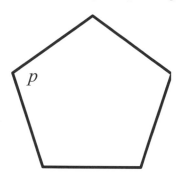

$p =$ _____ ° [1]

ⓒ Answer these questions. You do not need to show your workings out.
Diagrams not drawn to scale.

1 Find the missing angle x.

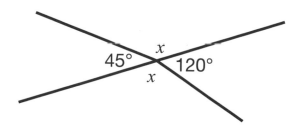

$x =$ _____ ° [1]

4

2 Find the missing angle x.

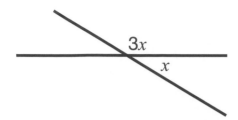

$x =$ _____° [1]

3 Find the missing angle x.

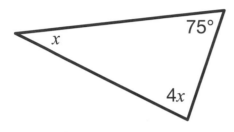

$x =$ _____° [1]

4 Find the missing angle y.

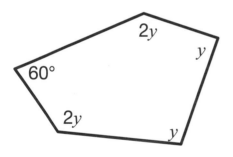

$y =$ _____° [1]

5 Find the missing angle y.

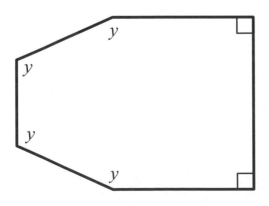

$y =$ _____° [1]

4

Geometry: properties of circles

Examples

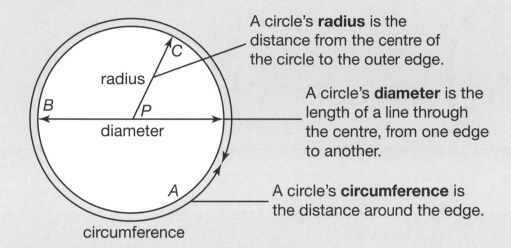

A circle's **radius** is the distance from the centre of the circle to the outer edge.

A circle's **diameter** is the length of a line through the centre, from one edge to another.

A circle's **circumference** is the distance around the edge.

1 What is the radius of a circle if the diameter is 7.5 cm?

Method:

The diameter is twice the radius so we need to divide the diameter by two.

Answer:

7.5 ÷ 2 = 3.75 cm

2 What is the name of the line PC?

Answer:

Radius

3 What is the name of the line C to C via A and B?

Answer:

Circumference

(A) Answer these questions. You do not need to show your workings out.

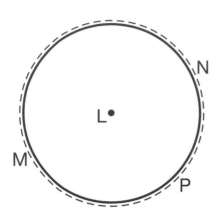

1 What is the name of line *MN*? _____ [1]

2 What is the name of line *LP*? _____ [1]

3 What is the name of line *N* to *N* via *P* and *M* on the outside of the circle? _____ [1]

4 If *LP* is 12.4 cm, find *LN*. _____ cm [1]

5 If *LP* is 12.4 cm, find *MN*. _____ cm [1]

6

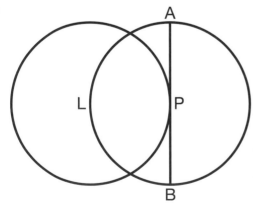

Line *AB* is 23.6 cm.

What is the radius of the left-hand circle? _____ cm [1]

6

Ⓑ Answer these questions.

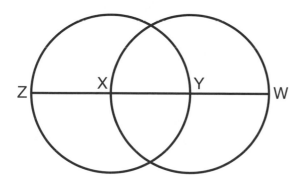

1 What is the name of line XY? _____ [1]

2 The line WZ is 1.086 m.
What is the distance from X to Y in m? Show your working out.

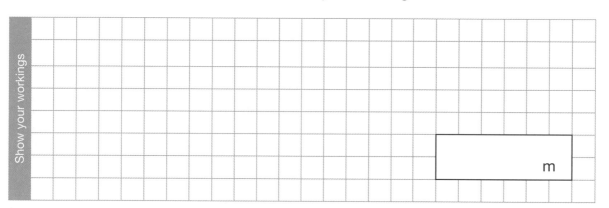

m [1]

3 The line WZ is 1.086 m.
What is the distance from X to W in cm? Show your working out.

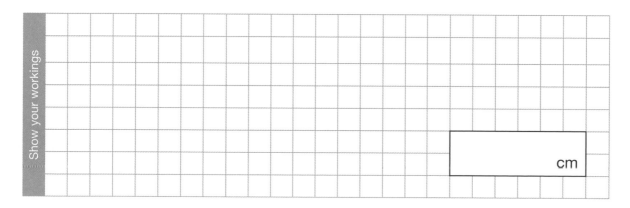

cm [1]

3

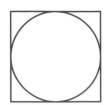

4 The **area** of the square is 100 cm².
What is the radius of the circle? Show your working out.

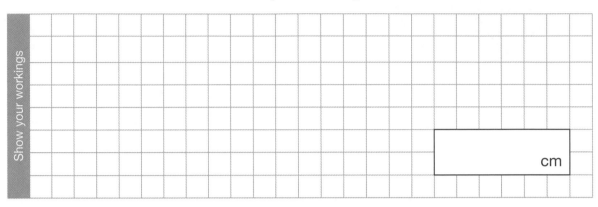

cm [1]

5 What is the name of the line around the circle that touches the square at four points ?

[1]

ⓒ Answer these questions. You do not need to show your workings out.

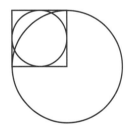

1 The diameter of the larger circle is 19.4 cm.
What is the area of the square? _____ cm² [1]

2 What is the radius of the smaller circle? _____ cm [1]

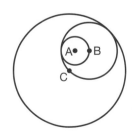

3 The diameter of the middle-sized circle is 14.6 cm.
What is the diameter of the largest circle? _____ cm [1]

4 What is the radius of the smallest circle? _____ cm [1]

6

Measurement: metric and imperial units

💡 **Helpful Hint**

The key metric conversions:	The key metric to **imperial** conversions:
1 litre = 100 centilitres = 1000 millilitres 1 kilograms = 1000 grams 1 kilometre = 1000 metres 1 metre = 100 centimetres = 1000 millimetres 1 day = 24 hours 1 hour = 60 minutes 1 minute = 60 seconds	16 kilometres ≈ 10 miles 30 grams ≈ 1 ounce

(A) Answer these questions. You do not need to show your workings out.

1 Convert 12.4 litres into cl. _____cl ☐ [1]

2 Convert 0.543 cl into ml. _____ml ☐ [1]

3 Convert 496 g into kg. _____kg ☐ [1]

4 Convert 21.04 km into m. _____m ☐ [1]

5 Convert 243.1 mm into cm. _____cm ☐ [1]

6 Convert $3\frac{1}{2}$ days into hours. _____hours ☐ [1]

7 Convert 332 minutes into hours. _____hours _____ minutes ☐ [1]

8 Approximately how far is 45 miles in km? _____km ☐ [1]

9 Approximately how many grams are in 110 oz? _____oz ☐ [1]

9

Unit 5

Ⓑ Answer these questions and show your workings out.

1

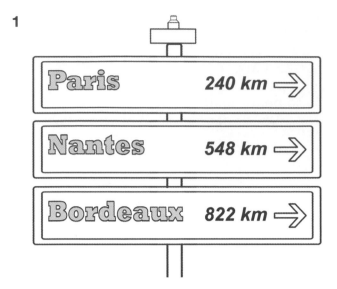

Roughly how far is it to Paris in miles?

Show your workings

			miles

[1]

2

Pancakes

For this recipe, you will need:

4 oz plain flour, sifted
Pinch of salt
1 egg
$\frac{1}{2}$ pt milk
2 oz butter

This recipe is for 6 pancakes.
Approximately how many grams of flour are required to make 9 pancakes?

Show your workings

[1]

2

3 Jasmin has a 2 litre bottle of cola and fills six 30 cl glasses.
How many millilitres of cola are left in the bottle?

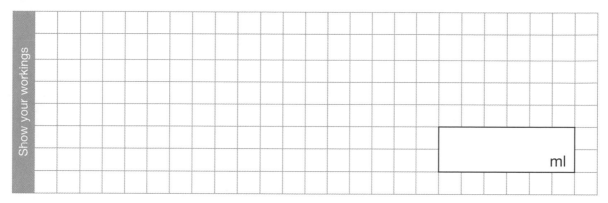

Show your workings

ml

[1]

4

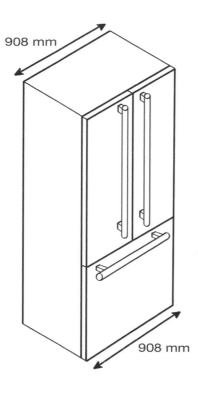

908 mm

908 mm

The new cupboard is 908 mm wide.
The gap it needs to fit in is 1 m wide.
Will the cupboard fit and if so, how much extra space is there in metres?

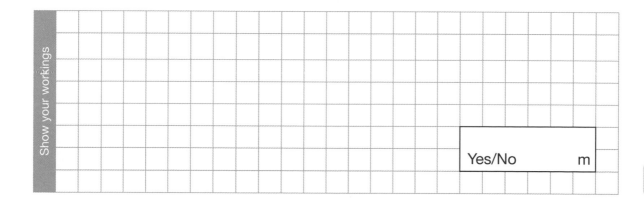

Show your workings

Yes/No   m

[1]

2

ⓒ Answer these questions. You do not need to show your workings out.

1 Convert 14 ml into litres. _____l ☐ [1]

2 Convert 0.04125 litre into ml. _____ml ☐ [1]

3 Convert 49 600 cm into km. _____km ☐ [1]

4 Convert 0.020179 m into mm. _____mm ☐ [1]

5 Convert 2 431 000 mm into km. _____km ☐ [1]

6 Convert $\frac{11}{4}$ days into minutes. _____minutes ☐ [1]

7 Convert 25 200 seconds into hours. _____hr ☐ [1]

8 Approximately how far is 52 miles in m? _____m ☐ [1]

9 Approximately how many ounces are in 525 grams? _____oz ☐ [1]

9

Answers

Unit 1

A

1 isosceles triangle
2 rectangle
3 heptagon
4 sphere
5 12
6 cylinder

B

1 kite
2 square
3 trapezium
4

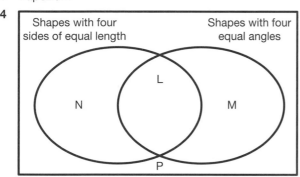

5 kite, rhombus, square

C

1 square-based pyramid
2 parallelogram
3 cone or hemisphere
4 triangular-based pyramid or tetrahedron
5 square, rhombus and kite

Unit 2

A

1 3.5 cm
2

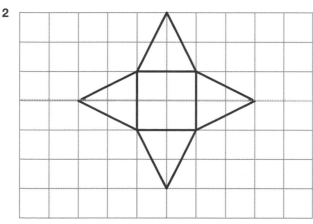

3 8.5 cm

B

1 4.6 cm
2 $6 \times (2 \times 2) = 6 \times 4 = 24$ cm^2
3 $2 \times (2 \times 2) = 2 \times 4 = 8$ cm^2
4 R
5 P

C

1 5.2 cm
2 $2 \times (1.5 \times 2) + 2 \times (1.5 \times 3) + 2 \times (2 \times 3) = 6 + 9 + 12 = 27$ cm^2
3 $1.5 \times (2 \times 3) = 1.5 \times 6 = 9$ cm^3
4 C
5 F

Unit 3

A

1 $x + 100 + 120 + 40 = 360$ so $x = 100°$
2 $y + 33 + 57 + 82 = 180$ so $y = 8°$
3 $p + 71 + 59 = 180$ so $p = 50°$
4 $x + 47 + 53 + 110 = 360$ so $x = 150°$
5 $x + 105 + 105 + 165 + 85 + 145 = 720$ so $x = 115°$

B

1 $x + 62 + 18 + x = 180$ so $2x = 100$ so $x = 50°$
2 $x = 33$ so $y = 180 - 33 = 147°$
3 $x + 111 + x + 111 = 360$ so $2x = 138$ so $x = 69°$
4 $5p = 540$ so $p = 108°$

C

1 $x + 45 + 120 + x = 360$ so $2x = 195$ so $x = 97.5°$
2 $x + 3x = 180$ so $4x = 180$ and $x = 45°$
3 $x + 4x + 75 = 180$ so $5x = 105$ and $x = 21°$
4 $y + 2y + 2y + y + 60 = 540$ so $6x = 480$ so $x = 80°$
5 $y + 90 + 90 + y + y + y = 720$ so $4x = 540$ so $y = 135°$

Unit 4

A

1 diameter
2 radius
3 circumference
4 12.4 cm
5 24.8 cm
6 $23.6 \div 2 = 11.8$ cm

B

1 radius
2 1.086 ÷ 3 = 0.362 m
3 0.362 × 2 = 0.724 m = 72.4 cm
4 10 × 10 = 100 so the diameter is 10 cm
   then 10 ÷ 2 = 5 cm
5 circumference

C

1 19.4 ÷ 2 = 9.7 then 9.7 × 9.7 = 94.09 cm²
2 19.4 ÷ 2 = 9.7 then 9.7 ÷ 2 = 4.85 cm
3 14.6 × 2 = 29.2 cm
4 14.6 ÷ 2 = 7.3 then 7.3 ÷ 2 = 3.65 cm

Unit 5

A

1 12.4 l × 100 = 1240 cl
2 0.543 cl × 10 = 5.43 ml
3 496 g ÷ 1000 = 0.496 kg
4 21.04 km × 1000 = 21 040 m
5 243.1 mm ÷ 10 = 24.31 cm
6 $3\frac{1}{2}$ × 24 = 84 hrs
7 332 ÷ 60 = 5 hrs 32 mins
8 45 ÷ 10 × 16 = 72 km
9 110 oz × 30 = 3300 g

B

1 240 km ÷ 16 × 10 = 150 miles
2 4 oz × 30 = 120 g then 120 ÷ 6 × 9 = 180 g
3 30 cl = 300 ml so 2 000 − 6 × 300 = 200 ml
4 yes; 1 m − 0.908 m = 0.092 m

C

1 14 ml ÷ 1000 = 0.014 l
2 0.04125 × 1000 = 41.25 ml
3 49 600 cm ÷ 100 ÷ 1000 = 0.496 km
4 0.020179 m × 1000 = 20.179 mm
5 2 431 000 mm ÷ 1000 ÷ 1000 = 2.431 km
6 $\frac{11}{4}$ days = $2\frac{3}{4}$ × 24 = 66 hrs × 60 = 3960 mins
7 25 200 secs ÷ 60 ÷ 60 = 7 hrs
8 52 miles ÷ 10 × 16 × 1000 = 83 200 m
9 525 g ÷ 30 = 17.5 oz

Unit 6

A

1 $\sqrt{25}$ = 5 then 5 × 4 = 20 cm
2 16 ÷ 2 = 8 then 2 + 2 + 8 + 8 = 20 cm
3 7 × 5 = 35 cm²
4 6 × 5 × 5 = 150 cm²
5 $\frac{1}{2}$ × 3 × 8 = 3 × 4 = 12 cm²

B

1 360 ÷ 2 = 180 then 180 − 110 = 70 m so width = 70 m;
   area = 110 × 70 = 7700 m²
2 $\frac{1}{2}$ × 4.5 × 17 = 38.25 m²
3 $A = w \times l + w \times h + 2 \times l \times s = 6 \times 12 + 6 \times 4 + 2 \times$
   12 × 5 = 72 + 24 + 120 = 216 cm²
4 450 ÷ 15 = 30 then 15 + 15 + 30 + 30 = 90 m

C

1 52 ÷ 4 = 13 then 13 × 13 = 169 cm²
2 108 ÷ 2 = 54 so width = 54 − 37 = 17 m then
   area = 37 × 17 = 629 m²
3 5.6 × 3 = 16.8 cm²
4 6 × 1.2 × 1.2 = 8.64 m²
5 $\frac{1}{2}$ × 26 × 73 = 949 cm²

Unit 7

A

1 7 × 4 × 2 = 56 cm³
2 1.5 × 6 × 4 = 36 m³
3 3 × 3 × 3 = 27 so length = 3 mm
4 10 × 4 = 40 cm³
5 15 × 3.5 = 52.5 cm³
6 $\frac{1}{3}$ × 12 × 3 = 12 mm³

B

1 (4 × 4 × 4) − (3 × 3 × 3) = 37
2 Cuboid B since A: 6 × 4 × 5 = 120; B: 2 × 7 × 8 = 112
3 $\frac{1}{2}$ × 3 × 4 × 10 = 60 m³
4 $\frac{1}{2}$ × 3 × 4 × 6 = 36 cm³
5 $\frac{1}{3}$ × 200 × 200 × 150 = 2 000 000 m³
6 $\frac{3}{4}$ × 3.2 × 9 = 21.6 cm³

Ⓒ

1 $40 \times 40 \times 40 = 64\,000$ mm³
2 $2 \times 3 \times 10 = 60$ cm³
3 $3 \times 3 \times 3 - (0.5 \times 0.5 \times 0.5) = 26.875$ cm³
4 $96 \div 6 = 16$ and $16 = 4 \times 4$ so $V = 4^3 = 64$ cm³
5 $h = 4500$ cm $\div 3000$ cm $= 1.5$ cm

Unit 8

Ⓐ

1 $282 \div 1.41 = £200$
2 $3 \times 15 = 45$ feet
3 $4.55 \times 2 = 9.1$ and $4.55 \times 20 = 91$ so $4.55 \times 22 = 100.1$ l
4 $7.8 \div 2.2 = 3.54$ kg
5 $250 \times 1.23 = €307.50$
6 $2.5 \times 568 = 1420$ ml

Ⓑ

1 $2 \times 8 + 3 = 19$ furlongs
2 $\frac{1}{2} \times 12 \times 4.55 = 27.3$ l
3 $749\,700 \div 1.4 = £535\,500$
4 $3.3 \times 8848 = 29\,198.4$ ft

Ⓒ

1 $380.70 \div 1.41 = £270$
2 $23 \times 3 + \frac{1}{3} \times 3 = 69 + 1 = 70$ feet
3 $80.16 \div 8 = 10.02$ gallons
4 $324 \div 1.2 = 270$ then $270 \times 1.45 = \$391.50$
5 $16 \times 28.4 = 454.4$ ml
6 12 inches $\times$ 2.5 cm per inch $= 30$ cm
7 100 cm $\div$ 2.5 cm per inch $= 40$ inches
8 5 feet $\times$ 12 inches per foot $\times$ 2.5 cm per inch
   $= 150$ cm or, using the answer from Question 6:
   5 feet $\times$ 30 cm per foot $= 150$ cm

Unit 9

1–3

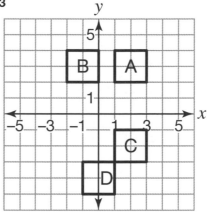

4–6

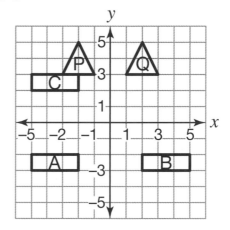

Ⓑ

1–3

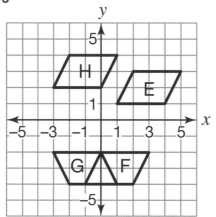

4–6

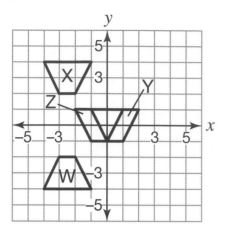

(C)

1–3

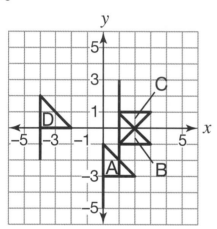

4–6

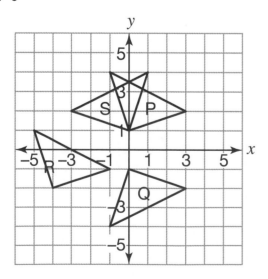

Unit 10

(A)

1 50

2 scooter; 25 people

3 4 × 100 = 400

4 Tuesday

5 22 – 10 = 12°C

6 $\frac{12 + 10 + 14 + 18 + 22}{5} = \frac{76}{5} = 15.2°C$

(B)

1 85 – 30 = 55

2 45 + 60 + 75 = 180

3 $\frac{30 + 85 + 180}{5} = \frac{295}{5} = 59$

4 10%

5 100 – 10 – 10 – 60 – 5 = 15%

6 5% = 75 so 10% = 150 then 100% = 1500 mins or 25 hrs

(C)

1

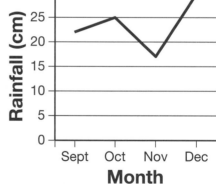

2 17 mm in the month of November

3 25 + 17 + 30 = 72 mm

4 $\frac{22 + 72}{4} = \frac{94}{4} = 23.5$ mm

Unit 6

Measurement: area and perimeter

 Helpful Hint

To find the **perimeter** of a square from its area, first find the length of each side. The perimeter is four times the length of a side.

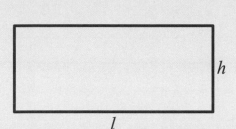

Area = length × height

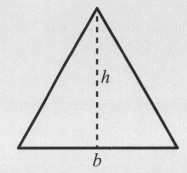

Area = $\frac{1}{2}$ × base × height

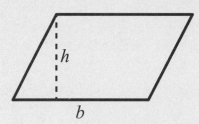

Area = base × **perpendicular** height

Here are the main formulae you need for this unit. You also need to know that the perimeter is the total distance around a shape.

Ⓐ Answer these questions. You do not need to show your workings out.

1 The area of a square is 25 cm².
What is the perimeter of the square? _____ cm ▢ [1]

2 The area of a rectangle is 16 cm².
The width of the rectangle is 2 cm.
What is the perimeter? _____ cm ▢ [1]

3 What is the area of a parallelogram with length
7 cm and perpendicular height 5 cm? _____ cm² ▢ [1]

3

4 The formula for the surface area of a cube is $A = 6 \times \text{length}^2$.
   What is the surface area of a cube with length 5 cm? _____cm² [1]

5 The formula for the area of a kite is $A = \frac{1}{2} \times \text{width} \times \text{height}$.
   What is the area of a kite with width 3 cm and height 8 cm? _____cm² [1]

Ⓑ Answer these questions and show your workings out.

1 The length of the local football pitch is 110 m. The perimeter is 360 m.

   What is the width of the pitch? _____m

   What is the area of the pitch? _____m² [2]

Show your workings

[1]

2
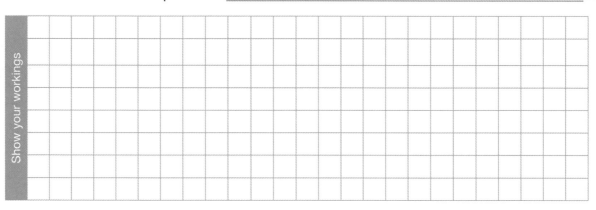

   What is the area of the triangular sail on this yacht?

Show your workings

m²

[1]

6

Helpful Hint

Make sure that all your answer measurements are in the same units.
Look out for g and kg or cm and km being mixed in questions.

3

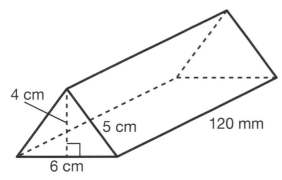

4 cm
5 cm
120 mm
6 cm

The formula for the surface area of a triangular prism is: $A = w \times l + w \times h + 2 \times l \times s$
Find the surface area.

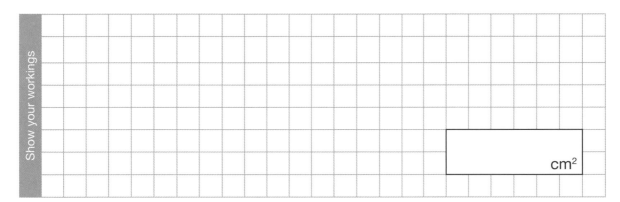

Show your workings

cm²

[1]

4

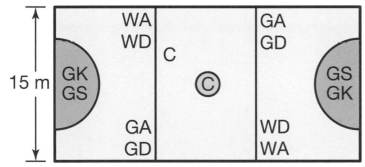

15 m

WA
WD
C
GA
GD
GK
GS
C
GS
GK
GA
GD
WD
WA

The width of a netball court is 15 m.
The area is 450 m².
What is the perimeter of the court?

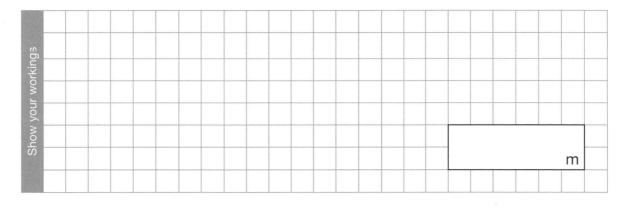

Show your workings

m

[1]

2

ⓒ Answer these questions. You do not need to show your workings out.

1 The perimeter of a square is 52 cm.
What is the area of the square?

_____ cm² ☐ [1]

2 The perimeter of a rectangle is 108 m.
The length is 37 m.
What is the area of the rectangle?

_____ m² ☐ [1]

3 What is the area of a parallelogram with length 5.6 cm and height 3 cm?

_____ cm² ☐ [1]

4 The formula for the surface area of a cube is $A = 6 \times \text{length}^2$.
What is the surface area of a cube with length 1.2 m?

_____ m² ☐ [1]

5 The formula for the area of a kite is $A = \frac{1}{2} \times \text{width} \times \text{height}$.
What is the area of a kite with width 26 cm and height 73 cm?

_____ cm² ☐ [1]

5

Measurement: volume of cuboids

Examples

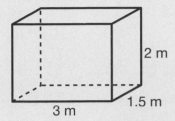

2 m

1.5 m

3 m

1 Find the volume of the cuboid. Give your answer in m³.

Method:

Multiply all three measurements to find the volume.

Volume = length × width × height
(in any order)
= 3 × 1.5 × 2
= 9 m³

2 The formula for the volume of a prism is

$V = $ **cross-sectional area** × length

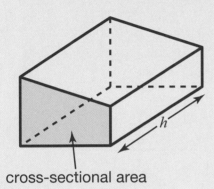

h

cross-sectional area

Find the volume when the cross-sectional area is 24 cm² and the length is 5 cm.

V = cross-sectional area × length
= 24 × 5
= 120 cm³

A good tip is to convert all the measurements into the units required before doing your calculation.

(A) Answer these questions. You do not need to show your workings out.

1 Find the volume of a cuboid with sides 7 cm, 4 cm and 2 cm. Give your answer in cm³. _____ cm³ ☐ [1]

2 Find the volume of a cuboid with sides 1.5 m, 6 m and 4 m. Give your answer in m³. _____ m³ ☐ [1]

3 The volume of a cube is 27 mm³. What is the length of each side? _____ mm ☐ [1]

4 Find the volume of a prism with a cross-sectional area of 10 cm² and length of 4 cm. _____ cm³ ☐ [1]

5 Find the volume of a prism with a cross-sectional area of 15 cm² and length of 3.5 cm. _____ cm³ ☐ [1]

 5

Helpful Hint

Volume of a square-based pyramid = $\frac{1}{3}$ × base area × height = $\frac{1}{3}$ × base × base × height

6 Find the volume of a square-based pyramid with base area 12 mm² and height 3 mm.

_____mm³ [1]

Ⓑ Answer these questions and show your workings out.

1 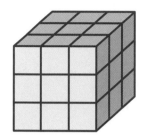 The shape is made from 1 cm cubes.
What is the smallest number of 1 cm cubes that need to be added to the shape to make a larger cube?

Show your workings

[1]

2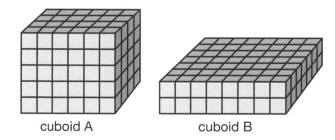

cuboid A   cuboid B

The shapes are made from 1 cm cubes. Which shape has the smaller volume?

Show your workings

[1]

3

3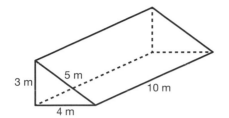

A cuboid has been cut in half diagonally.
Find the volume of this new shape.

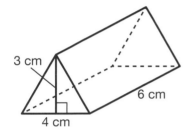

m³

[1]

4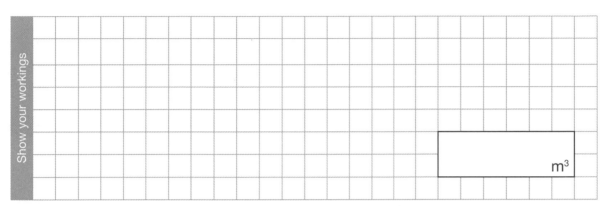

Find the volume of this triangular prism in cm³.

cm³

[1]

5 The pyramid of Khufu in Egypt has a height of approximately 150 m and the square base is approximately 200 m in length. Find the volume.

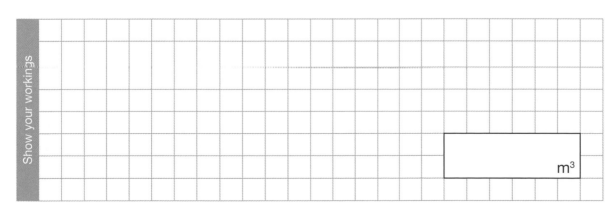

m³

[1]

3

6 The approximate volume of a banana is $= \frac{3}{4} \times$ width $\times$ length.

Find the volume of a banana with length 9 cm and width 3.2 cm.

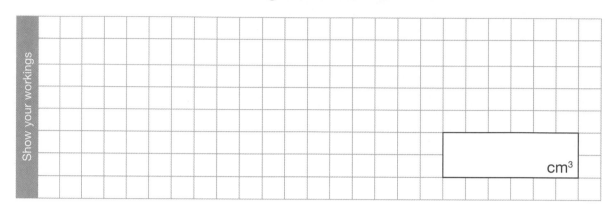

cm³

[1]

ⓒ Answer these questions. You do not need to show your workings out.

1

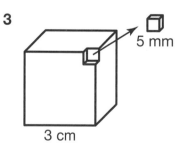

4 cm

Find the volume of the cube in mm³.

_____mm³ [1]

2

0.1 m
3 cm
20 mm

Find the volume of the cuboid in cm³.

_____cm³ [1]

3

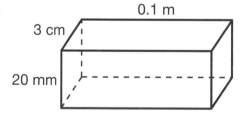

5 mm

3 cm

A cube of side length 3 cm has a smaller cube of side length 5 mm removed as shown.
What is the volume of the remaining shape?
Give your answer in cm³.

_____cm³ [1]

4 The total surface area of a cube is 96 cm².
Find the volume of the cube in cm³.

_____cm³ [1]

5 A triangular-based prism has cross-sectional
area 4500 cm². The volume is 3000 cm³.
Find the height in cm.

_____cm³ [1]

6

Measurement: problems involving conversion

Examples	Method:	Answer:
1 £1 = $1.40 What is £450 worth in $?	Multiply 450 by 1.40	$630
2 £1 = €1.20 What is €360 worth in £?	**Method:** Divide 360 by 1.20	**Answer:** £300

(A) Answer these questions. You do not need to show your workings out.

1 What is $282 in £ if the
exchange rate is £1 = $1.41?

£ _____ [1]

2 There are approximately 3 feet in a metre.
How many feet are in 15 metres?

_____ feet [1]

3 There are 4.55 litres in a gallon.
How many litres are in 22 gallons?

_____ l [1]

4 There are 2.2 pounds in a kg.
How many kg are in 7.8 pounds?

_____ kg [1]

5 £1 = €1.23
What is £250 worth in €?

€ _____ [1]

6 There are 568 ml in a pint.
How many ml in $2\frac{1}{2}$ pints?

_____ ml [1]

6

Ⓑ Answer these questions and show your workings out.

1 There are 8 furlongs in a mile.
A horse race is 2 miles and 3 furlongs long.
How many furlongs is this in total?

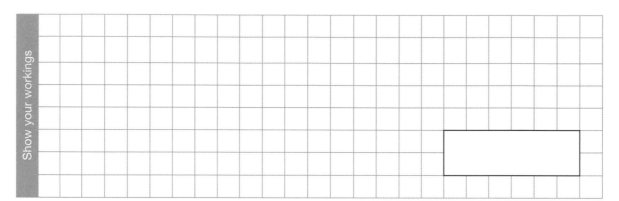

[1]

2

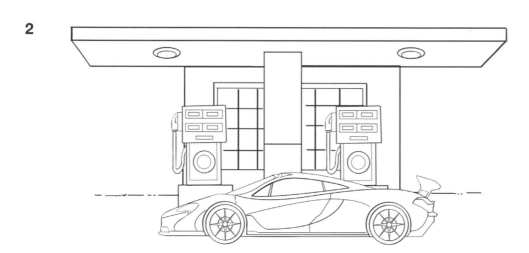

Gavin's new car has a 12 gallon fuel tank.
The car was half full of fuel when he got it.
How many litres of fuel are in the tank?

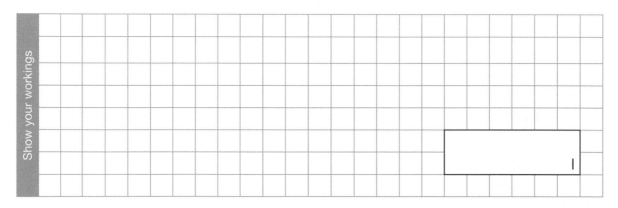

[1]

2

3

On holiday in France Maria saw a beautiful house for sale by the sea.
It was on sale for €749 700.
If £1 = €1.40, how much is this house worth in £?

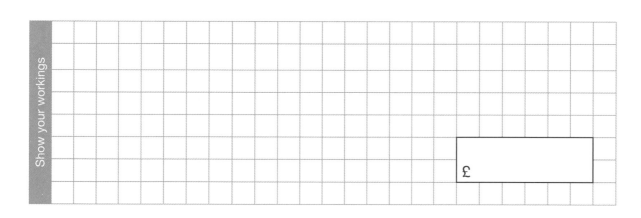

£

[1]

4 Mount Everest is 8848 m high.
How high is this in feet if there are 3.3 feet in a metre?

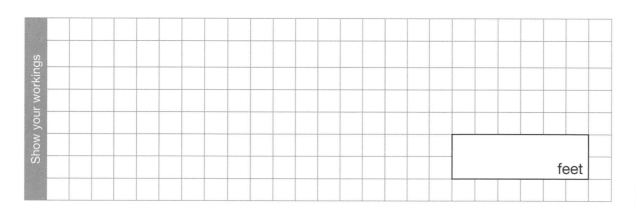

feet

[1]

2

ⓒ Answer these questions. You do not need to show your workings out.

1 What is $380.70 in £ if the exchange rate is £1 = $1.41?   £ _____ ☐ [1]

2 There are approximately 3 feet in a metre.
How many feet in $23\frac{1}{3}$ metres?   _____feet ☐ [1]

3 There are 8 pints in a gallon.
How many gallons are equal
to 80.16 pints?   _____ gallons ☐ [1]

4 £1 = €1.20
£1 = $1.45
What is €324 worth in $? $ _____ ☐ [1]

5 There are 28.4 ml in a fluid ounce.
How many ml are in 16 fl oz?   _____ ml ☐ [1]

If an inch is 2.5 cm and there are 12 inches in a foot, what is the answer to each
of these questions?

6 How many centimetres are there in a foot?   _____ cm ☐ [1]

7 How many inches are in a metre?   _____ inches ☐ [1]

8 Zac is 5 feet tall. How tall is he in centimetres?   _____ cm ☐ [1]

8

Geometry: translations and reflections in all four quadrants

Examples

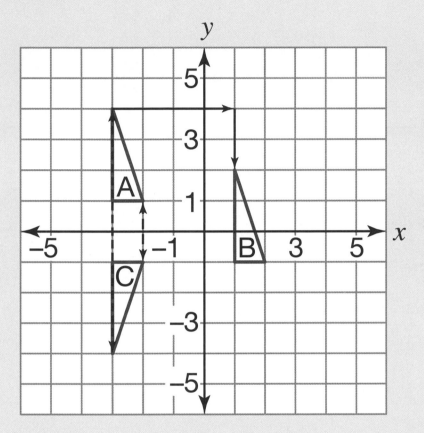

1 **Translate** triangle A 4 squares right and 2 down.

   Method:

   Move a key single point first then draw the rest of the **image**.

   Answer:

   Triangle B is the image.

2 **Reflect** triangle A in the x-axis.

   Method:

   Reflect two key single points first then draw the rest of the image.

   Answer:

   Triangle C is the image.

Ⓐ Answer these questions.

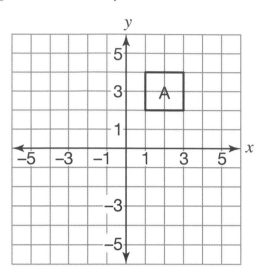

1 Translate square A 3 squares left. Label the image B. [1]

2 Translate square A 5 squares down. Label the image C. [1]

3 Translate square A 2 left and 7 squares down. Label the image D. [1]

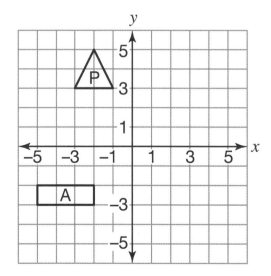

4 Reflect rectangle A in the y-axis. Label the image B. [1]

5 Reflect rectangle A in the x-axis. Label the image C. [1]

6 Reflect triangle P in the y-axis. Label the image Q. [1]

 6

Ⓑ Answer these questions.

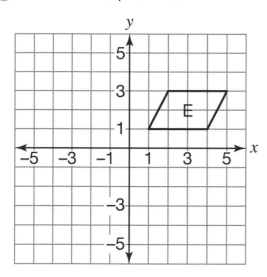

1 Translate parallelogram E 2 squares left and 5 down. Label the image F. [1]

2 Reflect parallelogram F in the y-axis. Label the image G. [1]

3 Reflect parallelogram G in the x-axis. Label the image H. [1]

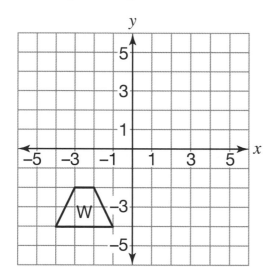

4 Reflect trapezium W in the x-axis. Label the image X. [1]

5 Translate trapezium X 3 squares right and 3 down. Label the image Y. [1]

6 Reflect trapezium Y in the y-axis. Label the image Z. [1]

6

ⓒ Answer these questions.

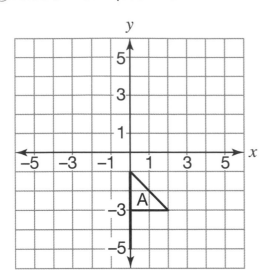

1 Translate flag A 1 square right and 2 up. Label the image B.   [1]

2 Reflect flag B in the x-axis. Label the image C.   [1]

3 Translate flag A 4 squares left and 3 up. Label the image D.   [1]

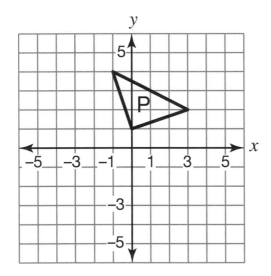

4 Reflect triangle P in the x-axis. Label the image Q.   [1]

5 Translate triangle P 4 squares left and 3 down. Label the image R.   [1]

6 Reflect triangle P in the y-axis. Label the image S.   [1]

6

Statistics

Examples

1   **Number of pupils in class 6HB**

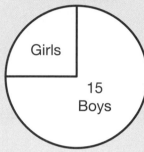

If there are 15 boys in the class, how many pupils are there all together?
How many girls are in the class?

Method:

$\frac{3}{4}$ of the class are boys so $\frac{1}{4}$ of the class is 5 pupils.
This means that there are 20 pupils in total.

Answer:

20 pupils total;
5 girls

2   Four pupils are aged 10, 8, 12 and 6. What is their **mean** age?

Method:

$$\text{mean} = \frac{\text{sum of all values}}{\text{number of values}}$$

Answer:

$$\text{mean} = \frac{10 + 8 + 12 + 6}{4} = \frac{36}{4} = 9$$

Ⓐ Answer these questions. You do not need to show your workings out.

Transport used to get to school

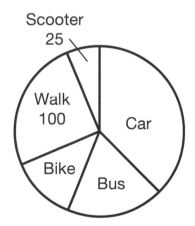

1   Using a protractor, calculate how many pupils went to school by bike. _____ [1]

2   Which is the least popular form of transport and how many pupils used it? _____ [1]

3   How many pupils does the pie chart represent in total? _____ [1]

3

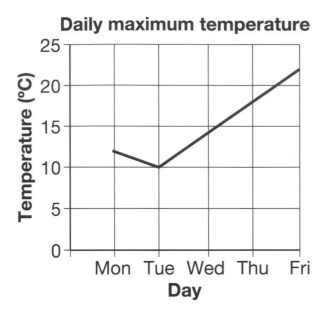

Daily maximum temperature

4 Which day had the lowest temperature? _____ [1]

5 What is the difference between the
highest and lowest temperature? _____ °C [1]

6 What was the mean temperature for
all 5 days? _____ °C [1]

Ⓑ Use the information below to answer these questions and show your workings out.

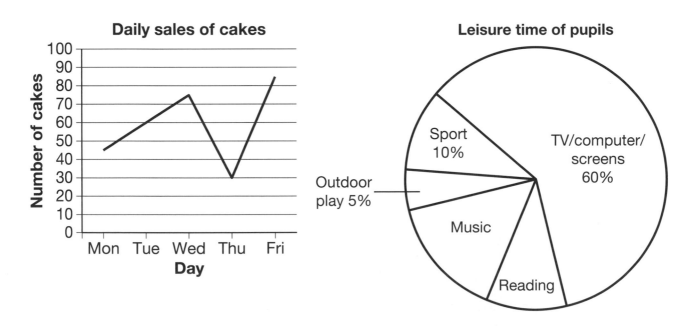

Daily sales of cakes

Leisure time of pupils

3

1 How many more cakes were sold on Friday than Thursday?

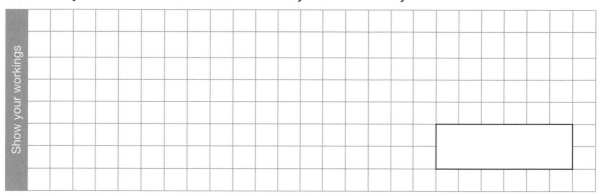

[1]

2 What was the total number of cakes sold on the first 3 days of the week?

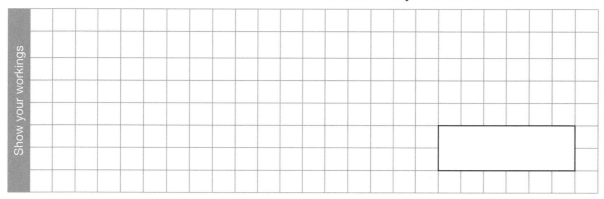

[1]

3 What was the mean number of cakes sold from Monday to Friday **inclusive**?

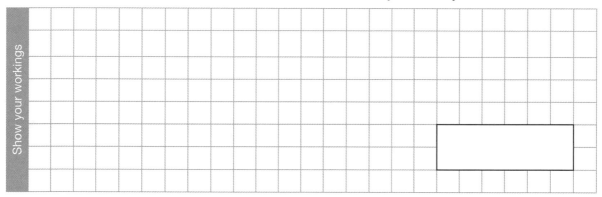

[1]

4 What percentage of leisure time was spent on reading? _____ %   [1]

5 What percentage of leisure time was spent on music?

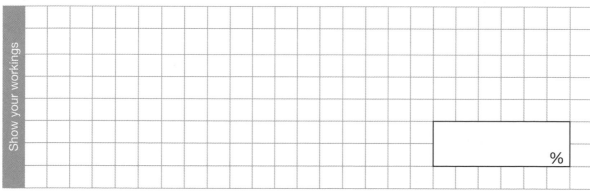

%

[1]

5

6 75 minutes were spent on outdoor play.
What is the total time spent on all the activities?

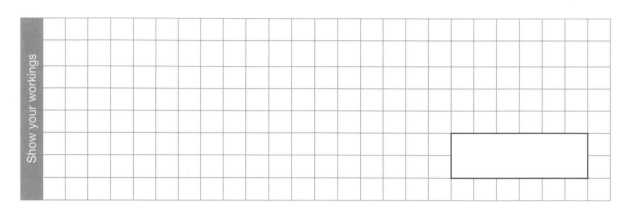

Show your workings

[1]

Ⓒ Answer these questions. You do not need to show your workings out.

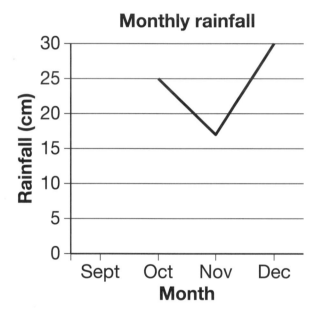

Monthly rainfall

1 There were 22 mm of rainfall in September. Mark this on the line graph and join up the line.

[1]

2 What was the lowest rainfall and in which month?

_____ mm in the month of _____

[2]

3 What was the total rainfall from
October to December inclusive? _____mm

[1]

4 What was the mean rainfall from
September to December inclusive? _____mm

[1]

6

Key Words

≈ approximately equal to and is sometimes used when rounding numbers

adjacent next to each other

area the size of a surface or the space inside the boundary of a flat object

circumference the distance around the edge of a circle

convert to change from one unit to another

cross-sectional area when a prism is chopped up into pieces the cross-sectional area remains constant

diameter the line joining two points on the circumference of a circle through the centre

edge the name of a line between two faces

face the name given to a flat surface of a solid object

image the shape after a transformation

inclusive the values mentioned at either end should be included

mean a type of average (value around which a group of values are centred)

parallelogram a four-sided shape with two pairs of parallel sides and equal opposite angles

perpendicular at right angles to another line or surface

perimeter the total distance around a shape

prism a solid shape with a uniform cross section

radius the distance from the centre of a circle to the circumference

reflect/reflection a transformation (a move or change in the shape and/or position of an object) in a line of reflection (mirror line)

surface area the area covering the outside of an object

translate/translation moving a shape in a direction without changing the original shape

Venn diagram a diagram representing sets pictorially as circles within an enclosing area, with common elements of the sets being represented by intersections of the circles

volume the amount of 3-dimensional space an object takes up

Progress chart

Bond SATs Skills Maths Workbook – Measurement, Geometry & Statistics 10–11

How did you do? Fill in your score below and shade in the corresponding boxes to compare your progress across the different tests and units.

50%   100%   50%   100%

Unit 1, p4 Score __ / 6

Unit 6, p28 Score __ / 6

Unit 1, p5 Score __ / 10

Unit 6, p29 Score __ / 2

Unit 1, p6 Score __ / 7

Unit 6, p30 Score __ / 5

Unit 2, p7 Score __ / 1

Unit 7, p31 Score __ / 5

Unit 2, p8 Score __ / 3

Unit 7, p32 Score __ / 3

Unit 2, p9 Score __ / 4

Unit 7, p33 Score __ / 3

Unit 2, p10 Score __ / 8

Unit 7, p34 Score __ / 6

Unit 3, p11 Score __ / 1

Unit 8, p35 Score __ / 6

Unit 3, p12 Score __ / 5

Unit 8, p36 Score __ / 2

Unit 3, p13 Score __ / 4

Unit 8, p37 Score __ / 2

Unit 3, p14 Score __ / 4

Unit 8, p38 Score __ / 8

Unit 4, p16 Score __ / 6

Unit 9, p40 Score __ / 6

Unit 4, p17 Score __ / 3

Unit 9, p41 Score __ / 6

Unit 4, p18 Score __ / 6

Unit 9, p42 Score __ / 6

Unit 5, p19 Score __ / 9

Unit 10, p43 Score __ / 3

Unit 5, p20 Score __ / 2

Unit 10, p44 Score __ / 3

Unit 5, p21 Score __ / 2

Unit 10, p45 Score __ / 5

Unit 5, p22 Score __ / 9

Unit 10, p46 Score __ / 6

Unit 6, p27 Score __ / 3